THE DEVON QUIZ BOOK

Margaret Caine and Alan Gorton

A COMFY JACK BOOK

To Marjorie,
whose considerable gifts and
kindness have contributed to this book.

First published in 2002 by Cotswold Quality (Leisure) Ltd,
4, Gables Court, Blackwell, Warwickshire CV36 4PE

ISBN 0 9541036 1 0

Cover designed by NPD Design Consultants, Shipston-on-Stour CV36 4AH
Printed and bound by R Booth (Bookbinder) & Troutbeck Press
Antron Hill, Mabe, Penryn, Cornwall TR10 9HH

CONTENTS

Front Cover: Waterwheel, Morwellham Quay; shepherds and sheep, Hatherleigh market; cliff railway, Lynton/Lynmouth
Title Page: The original gateway, Her Majesty's Prison, Dartmoor
Back Cover: Haldon Belvedere, Dunchideock; Old Mother Hubbard's show, Highwayman Inn, Sourton; harbour and Rhenish Tower, Lynmouth; medieval clapper bridge, Postbridge; St Mary Steps, Exeter; shepherds (rear view), Hatherliegh

INTRODUCTION

This book will appeal to all who care about the county of Devon, whether resident, visitor or those with a long-standing attachment. Devon has a style and a spirit, a tone and a tempo all of its own: but are you prepared to test your knowledge of its old market towns with their idiosyncratic features and historical riches, its villages of golden charm, its churches which are architectural jewels, its modern urban necessities of shopping centres and expressways, or where thirsts can be assuaged with a local brew? How well do you really know this most delightful of counties? *The Devon Quiz Book* challenges you to find out.

Quizzes are a popular pastime – at home, in the pub, with others or alone. It is fun to test your knowledge, tease your memory, and see how much you know. Everyone can join in, young and not-so-young alike. *The Devon Quiz Book* is guaranteed to keep you interested for hour after hour and at the same time give you an opportunity to learn more about where you live or spend your holidays.

The book covers a range of topics and subjects, and the questions are at different levels of difficulty. None are cryptic, none are misleading. We have selected carefully from the historical, geographical, agricultural, industrial, military, political and religious possibilities, and added questions about myths and legends, fairies and ghosts, food and fashions, rural and maritime traditions. There is more to this book, though. Many questions have longer-than-usual answers so you can learn about the county at the same time as searching your knowledge. Whether your interest is in bathing huts or theme parks, whether you seek Lorna Doone or cream teas, whether the landscape in which you find yourself is rural and idyllic, supporting a community of hard-working and home-loving men and women, or wild and remote, harbouring a motley collection of weird and treacherously suspect individuals who are the product of romantic novelists, this book will enable you to examine and improve your knowledge. The answers have been separated from the questions so you will not need a question master – unless you wish to appoint one.

The questions will certainly test your knowledge of this "*Shire of the Sea Kings*", and if they encourage you to research deeper into those topics where your interest has been stimulated or where your knowledge has been found wanting, we look forward to meeting you on your travels.

Margaret Caine and Alan Gorton

1 ANIMALS

"There are no woods nor copses other than one oake called Kite Oake and a few thornes growing here and there ... a large grounde many thousand acres in extent, time out of mind used for the pasture of great numbers of sheep, cattle and horse beasts..."

Report by a witness in a 1622 lawsuit describing the King's Forest of Exmoor.

1 Where is the only zoo in a National Park?

2 Where is the home of Devon's largest livestock market?

3 Who is Powderham Castle's oldest resident?

4 What animals can you see balancing atop impossibly narrow paths in the wind-carved Valley of Rocks, Lynton?

5 In what month are the Bicton Horse Trials held annually at East Bicton, Budleigh?

6 (a) Exmoor is the last secure haunt in England of which wild animal, Britain's largest mammal?
(b) How many are estimated to live in Exmoor National Park now?
(c) What is the 'head' of this animal and what are 'brow, bay and trey'?
(d) What name is given to the noise it makes?

7 Thousands of hedgehogs are injured or orphaned each year by cars, pesticides, bonfires or household refuse: which Devon hospital cares for and treats them?

8 Where is the world's largest donkey sanctuary, founded in 1969 and which has taken in more than 8,000 donkeys?

9 When the animals were evacuated from Chessington Zoo in World War II, where did they go?

10 (a) Where is the National Shire Horse Centre?
(b) Why is King, one of the Shires, noted in the *Guinness Book of Records*?

11 What is the connection between a smooth-haired, short-legged terrier and a Devon clergymen who was also a Master of Foxhounds?

12 What is the name of Devon's traditional cattle?

2 ARCHAEOLOGY

"The longer one stays here the more does the spirit of the moor sink into one's soul, its vastness, and also its grim charm. When you are once out upon its bosom you have left all traces of modern England behind you, but on the other hand you are conscious everywhere of the homes and the work of the prehistoric people. If you were to see a skin-clad, hairy man ... fitting a flint-tipped arrow on to the string of his bow, you would feel that his presence there was more natural than your own."

Arthur Conan Doyle, *The Hound of the Baskervilles*

1 Where is the ancient stone circle of Nine Stones - formed of nine maidens who were petrified after being discovered dancing on the Sabbath?

2 How tall is The Longstone on Exmoor?

3 Why outside Combe Martin is a stone known as the Hanging Stone?

4 Which two Iron Age tribes settled in Devon, before the arrival of the Romans?

5 One Iron Age fort on Exmoor consists of a square enclosure of almost five acres, with rounded corners, and ramparts about eight feet high. Which?

6 What is the name given to the Roman road which starts or finishes at Exeter, runs to Seaton and then north on through the country to Lincoln?

7 Where is Britain's oldest Scheduled Ancient Monument, dating back two million years, the site of the earliest evidence of human habitation and dwellings in Britain?

8 Where is the Brutus Stone and what is it used for?

9 Dartmoor granite has provided the material for marking the final resting place for people for hundreds of years. What is the most recent commemorative structure made of Dartmoor granite?

10 What is Grimspound, near Widecombe-in-the-Moor, on Dartmoor?

11 In 1913 a stone inscribed CAVUDI FILIUS CIVILI ((Cavidus, son of Civilus) was found serving as a gatepost. Where can you see it now?

12 A deterioration in the climate from *c*.1,000 to 500 BC saw the gradual depopulation of high Dartmoor: what is the only surviving evidence from then?

3 ART AND THE ARTS

Here lieth a blossom of the world's great tree
Who was as fair as buds of roses be,
She died an infant - Heaven was made for such,
Live like an infant, thou shalt have as much.

Epitaph to Anna Bartlett, died 1609, in
St Winifred's churchyard, Branscombe.

1 Name one of the two outdoor Sculpture Gardens in Devon.

2 On which beach did John Everett Millais paint 'The Boyhood of Raleigh'?

3 Beryl Cook and Robert Lenkiewicz are both local artists to ...?

4 Where is the Mythic Garden Sculpture Exhibition?

5 Where can you see a Georgian painting collection which includes ten works by Sir Joshua Reynolds?

6 On the cliff edge within Lee Abbey estate, Duty Point tower is depicted in one of the great landscape paintings of the early nineteenth century: who was the artist?

7 When visiting south Devon, J M W Turner created a painting, later to become famous, of a large vertical rock or stack on the shore with a hole through it: where is this rock, from which the village was named?

8 Where is the world's finest design and manufacturing base for teapots of every conceivable shape and size?

9 Where is the International Festival of Folk Arts held?

10 What is Exeter's West Quarter best known for?

11 Which bridge is said to have inspired the American entertainer Paul Simon to write his international success 'Bridge Over Troubled Water'?

12 Born in 1723 in Plympton Earls near Plymouth, the seventh son of a clergyman and schoolmaster, which artist founded the Literary Club in 1764, in 1768 was elected the first President of the Royal Academy, in 1769 was knighted, in 1784 became painter to the King, and is world famous for his portraits?

4 BIRDS AND BEASTS

"Exmoor is the high country of winds, which are to the falcons and the hawks; clothed by whortleberry bushes and lichens and ferns and mossed trees in the goyals, which are to the foxes, the badgers and red deer; served by rain clouds and drained by rock-littered streams, which are to the otters."

Henry Williamson, *Tarka the Otter*

1 Where will you find Dinosaurs in a park?

2 Where is the Gnome Reserve?

3 Where can you gain a fascinating insight into the life of the honey bee, with live exhibits, and the story of honey making?

4 Where is home to Dartford Warblers?

5 The RSPB has a nature reserve on the Exe estuary made up of two marshes: what are they?

6 What is the name of the bird-watching cruises up the River Exe estuary from Exmouth to see migrants from their harsh Arctic breeding grounds during their visit to this spectacular estuary?

7 Where is the Devon County Show held, and in which month of the year?

8 Where is an annual worm charming competition held?

9 Where can you see the first Red Kite on view to the public in the South West?

10 What is the connection between Kingsbridge, Montague's harrier and the cirl bunting?

11 Together with the kestrel, sparrow hawk and raven, which is the commonest of the larger birds of prey which can be seen on Exmoor?

12 The Large Blue Butterfly exists on only a handful of sites in the country, and one of these is in Devon. Where?

5 CASTLES

"Liberty is to be more desired than fetters of gold"
Michael Davitt, 1885, Former Dartmoor prisoner

1 Which restored castle is now a theme park?

2 Which castle was the home of Sir Humphrey Gilbert, coloniser of Newfoundland and half-brother of Sir Walter Raleigh, and used as location for the 1995 version of Jane Austen's *Sense and Sensibility*, starring Emma Thompson, Kate Winslet, Hugh Grant, Alan Rickman and Greg Wise?

3 In which castle, whose chapel is the oldest complete building in Devon, is there a *Mary Rose* and *Titanic* exhibition showing the family's connection with maritime history?

4 (a) Which castle is reputedly the most haunted in Devon?
(b) This castle was the former home of two influential families - what remains of the former homes of each family?

5 What is the connection between Tiverton Castle and a bride celebrating her marriage?

6 The granite Castle Drogo, overlooking the wooded gorge of the River Teign, was built between 1910 and 1930, thus making it England's last castle, and combines simulated 'medieval' grandeur with twentieth-century comforts.
(a) Who was the architect who designed it? (b) Who was the owner?

7 Dartmouth Castle, in a defensive situation jutting into the narrow entrance to the Dart estuary, was built when?

8 (a) How is Lawrence Castle otherwise known? (b) What is unusual about it?

9 Which castle was the family home of the Earls of Devon?

10 Which two castles are connected by the 'Two Castles Trail'?

11 What is the connection between Affeton Castle, Crediton, and Hartland Abbey?

12 Exeter Castle was built originally *c.*1068 by William the Conqueror, and continues one of its erstwhile functions: which?

6 CHURCHES

Hee first deceased her ..... For a while shee tryed
To live without him ..... Didn't like it, dyed!
Epitaph in Woodbury church.

1 Where is the tallest Bishop's Throne in England?

2 (a) Which Abbey is famous for producing honey and tonic wine?
(b) How long did it take just four monks to build the present Abbey Church?

3 The clock dial on the church of St Peter, Buckland-in-the-Moor, does not have conventional numbers. How does it read?

4 In which church will you find a list of instructions 'To the Conductors and Overseers of Waggons and Carts' on their duties in the event of an invasion by Napoleon's troops in 1804, which include 'the Removal of the Sick and Infirm' while taking care to 'avoid travelling upon the public Roads, which are to be left open for the King's Use, namely for the Conveyance of Ammunition and Provision for the Troops, and for their March', for which they must 'have proper Tools, for the purpose of making Breaches in Hedges, &c' ?

5 In which church do carved pew-ends depict village life of about 400 years ago?

6 Why is the rock on the steep path to the west of Sticklepath painted white?

7 (a) Which church is known as 'the Cathedral of Dartmoor'?
(b) What incident at this church was recorded in verse by the churchwardens and is displayed on boards in the tower?

8 Membury has two very similar church buildings: the parish church of St John - and which other?

9 Where is an astronomical clock built to work on the theory of Ptolemy?

10 (a) Henry Francis Lyte was vicar of All Saints church, Brixham, when in 1847 he wrote a hymn which was to become a favourite - what is it?
(b) Augustus Toplady wrote '*Rock of Ages*'- of where was he the vicar ?

11 Why is St Luke's church, Milber, Newton Abbot, called 'The Dream Church'?

12 (a) When was the building of Exeter Cathedral commenced?
(b) What is the name of the bell which hangs in the tower above the astronomical clock, and chimes the hours?

7 CUSTOMS

Here lies the body of Mary Sexton,
Who pleased many a man, but never vex'd one,
Not like the woman who lies under the next stone.

Epitaph in the churchyard at Bideford

1 Four towns in North Devon have 'pannier markets'. Name three of them.

2 A bizarre ritual is held at Combe Martin annually at the end of May. What is it?

3 (a) Where is Potwalloping held? (b) When is the Lympstone Furry Dance?

4 Where on Wednesdays throughout the summer do villagers dress in Georgian costume for the '1785 Day' Craft Market - with entertainment on the green?

5 (a) Underneath the pillared roof of the ancient Queen Anne's Walk, Barnstaple, is the unique 'Tome Stone': what was it used for?
(b) At Barnstaple's fair a proclamation is read in Guildhall by the town clerk, after which the 'Hand of Friendship' appears - what is this?

6 Widecombe Fair, made famous by the song, after which Old Tom Cobleigh and his notorious companions took a ride on a grey mare, is held when?

7 (a) Where and (b) when is The Running of the Black Dog?

8 (a) Where is the Flaming Tar Barrels Ceremony held, and Pixies roam earlier?
(b) In which other town are burning tar barrels used as part of its Carnival?

9 (a) Where does the Glove Ceremony mark the beginning of this famous annual fair, held in the first week of May?
(b) How in times past did people signal that they could sell liquor exempt from excise duty during the fair - a right which sadly no longer exists?
(c) During which annual fair can no man be arrested while a Glove is on display, and begins with hot coins being thrown to 'poor' children?

10 Where do the traditional annual events include the ancient Saxon ceremonies of election of the office of Portreeve (a local representative of the monarch) and a court leet with an Ale Taster, Bread Weigher and Tree Inspector?

11 Where, on November 5, is the Devil involved?

12 What are 'Dartmoor letter boxes'?

8 DARTMOOR

> *"I solemnly swear to you, Sir, nothing will ever induce me to set foot on Dartmoor again. If I chance to see it from the Hoe, Sir, I'll avert my eyes. How can people think to come here for pleasure - for pleasure, Sir! - only unwholesome-minded individuals can love Dartmoor."*
>
> Sabine Baring-Gould, *Book of Dartmoor*, 1900

1 What is the area of the elevated mass of granite designated a National Park?

2 (a) What is the highest point on Dartmoor, and how high is it above sea level?
(b) What is the second highest point on Dartmoor?

3 Where is the Dartmoor Hunt Point-to-Point Meeting held?

4 Small but incredibly hardy, adapted to the harsh and often wet conditions, Dartmoor ponies have grazed on the land that now forms the National Park for nearly 2,000 years, though they were first recorded in the will of the Saxon Bishop Aelfwold of Crediton.
(a) Approximately how many Dartmoor ponies now live in the National Park?
(b) Who owns them?
(c) To which organisation do these owners belong?

5 Becky Falls Woodland Park, at Manaton, near Bovey Tracey, is designated as both an AONB and an SSSI. What are these?

6 How does the famous beauty spot of Dartmeet get its name?

7 What is Bowerman's Nose?

8 Which village is considered to be at the centre of Dartmoor?

9 How many live military firing ranges are there on Dartmoor, what are their names, and what proportion of the total area of the National Park do they use?

10 'Dartmoor Granite' is a collective phrase as some 400 different types of granite have been identified within the moor.
(a) For which major constructions in London was Dartmoor granite used?
(b) Where and when did the last working Dartmoor quarry cease production?

11 What is notable about the spelling of Buckfastleigh?

12 Where is the oldest oak tree on Dartmoor?

9 EXMOOR

"Memerendum that the said Chace is a Mountenous and cold ground much be Clouded with thick Foggs and Mists ... a verrye great part theirof is overgrowne with heath, and yielding but a pore Kind of turf of Litle vallue ... the Residue theirof being only some of the Balls or Hills, if inclosed might bee capeable of Improvement being a good soyle."

Memorandum of a survey of Exmoor Chase, 1651

1 (a) When was Exmoor National Park formed and what is its area?
(b) What is the symbol which marks one's entry into Exmoor National Park?

2 The Warden of the Royal Forest of Exmoor was a hereditary position given to a courtier, and from 1508 leased out. How many females have held this title?

3 When John Knight bought the Crown's interests in the Royal Forest in 1819, he and his son Frederic built a wall around their new estate. How long was it?

4 From what Old English word is 'Lyn' of Lynmouth and Lynton derived?

5 Where is 'Mother Meldrum's Kitchen'?

6 What is the furthest point west of Exmoor?

7 Although it is the river Exe which gives its name to Exmoor, which is the longest river in the region?

8 What is County Gate?

9 The Exmoor pony is a unique breed; with only *c*.800 breeding ponies world-wide the population is less than that of many endangered species. It is hardy, shaggy-coated, and descended from those which survived the last Ice Age.
(a) What is the standard height of the Exmoor wild pony?
(b) What features distinguish this pony from others?
(c) When was the Exmoor Pony Society formed?

10 What is the name of the ancient breed of hardy sheep found in may parts of Exmoor?

11 Who was Fanny Pope, whose name is on a signpost at a crossroads on Exmoor?

12 Exmoor has two kinds of boggy areas, valley bogs and blanket bogs. What are the latter?

10 FILM AND TV

He is fortunate who can find an ideal England of the past, the present and the future ...and embody it in his native fields and waters, or his garden...
Edward Thomas, *The South Country*

1 The 1996 TV production of *Rebecca*, starring Charles Dance, Emilia Fox, Diana Rigg and Faye Dunaway, used which part of Devon for its location?

2 The 1997 TV version of *Tess of the D'Urbevilles* was filmed throughout Hardy's 'Wessex', but used some locations in Devon. Which?

3 What was the name of the 1998 film and TV production which used the Royal William Yard, Plymouth, as its location?

4 The 2000 and 2001 BBC TV series *Down to Earth* was filmed where?

5 In the 1968 film *Isadora*, starring Vanessa Redgrave and Jason Robards, the eccentric 1920s dancer Isadora Duncan relects on her unconventional life. Where was it filmed?

6 The BBC TV series of *Miss Marple*, which ran from 1986-1992, used several locations in Devon.
   (a) Which railway was used for scenes in *Sleeping Murder* of 1986?
   (b) What location was used for *Nemesis*, made in 1986?

7 Which Devon location featured in the pop videos by Pink Floyd's 'The Wall' and Robbie Williams's 'Angels'?

8 Which cove doubled as a Scottish harbour for the filming of *Kidnapped*?

9 Which country house, Devon's largest, became Norland Park, the Dashwood's family home, in the 1996 film of Jane Austen's *Sense and Sensibility*?

10 Which Devon location was used in the filming of 'The Onedin Line' to represent the port of Liverpool?

11 Which railway station has featured in many films and TV programmes, including *To Serve Them All My Days*, *A Horseman Riding By*, and *Penmarric*?

12 In the TV adaptation of R F Delderfield's *Diana*, the lovers used a small, square tower as a trysting-place. What and where is it?

11 ALL AT SEA

Our worthy friend who lies beneath this stone
Was master of a vessel all his own.
House and lands had he, and gold in store;
He spent the whole, and would if ten times more.
Epitaph for Captain Henry Clark, died 1836, at Bideford

1 Name two of the lighthouses off the Devon coast.

2 At Axminster in 1839 a massive eight million tons of rock tumbled seawards and formed the Undercliff. A hundred and forty years later these lime rich rocks became a location for which film?

3 What is the significance of the black and white galleon design on the ferry which plies across the estuary between Teignmouth and Shaldon?

4 What boats do Western Lady Ferries use, which will speed you down the coast to bustling Brixham?

5 (a) Name the two ships which originally set out from Plymouth with the 150 Pilgrim Fathers who made the 67-day journey to America.
(b) Where did the less well-known one have to put in for repairs after setting off from Plymouth?

6 Pete Goss's revolutionary catamaran, designed for the fastest circumnavigation by sail in 'The Race' of 2000, was built where?

7 What function does the Mariners' Chapel on Lantern Hill, Ilfracombe, serve?

8 What was the name of the lifeboat stationed at Lynmouth which in January 1899 had to be hauled by 100 men and 20 horses over Countisbury Hill to Porlock because the sea was too rough for the boat to be launched from home?

9 There are currently eight lifeboat stations in Devon.
(a) Name four of them. (b) Which is the oldest?

10 Where is the Maritime Trawler Race held?

11 Where in Devon is there an annual Royal Regatta, second only to Cowes?

12 Where can you embark on a replica of Francis Drake's ship, *Golden Hind*?

12 FOOD AND DRINK

Jan Roberts lives here,
Sells cider and beer
Your hearts to cheer.
And if you want meat
To make up a treat
Here be rabbits to eat.
Sign displayed by a nineteenth-century landlord of Warren House Inn, Dartmoor.

Underneath this crust
Lies the mouldering dust
Of Eleanor Batchelor Shoen
Well versed in the arts
Of pies, custards and tarts
And the lucrative trade of the oven
Epitaph, North Devon churchyard

1 Where is Clawford's Vineyard?

2 Where can you dine in a Carved Angel?

3 (a) Where is a 300-year-old wooden twin-screw cider press still in use today?
(b) Where can you buy Jack Ratt cider?

4 What are Peverstone's Hunting Pink, Devon Garland and Tisky Meadow?

5 Between which towns does the Riviera Dining Belle Train run?

6 What is the connection between Black Friars distillery, Plymouth, and Winston Churchill?

7 Langage Farm, Plympton, has won an award - for what?

8 What is the name of the cooperative which sells home-grown vegetarian fare at the Courtyard, Chagford?

9 In Butchers' Row, Barnstaple, over 300lbs of seaweed are sold each week in season. Why?

10 What is produced at The Big Sheep?

11 Which was the first Balti house in the West Country?

12 After the introduction of metrication, what was Inches Cider of Winkleigh known as?

13 GARDENS AND PLANTS

The Gardener at a hole looks out And holes are plenty hereabout
A pair of pistols by his lug One load with ball the other slug
A blunderbus of cannon shape Just ready to discharge with grape
Let midnight thief or robber stand And pause ere he puts out his hand
While those who come in open day May look but carry nought away.
Inscription on the Palm House, Bicton House, *c.*1850

1 The Royal Horticultural Society has established a garden of national importance at Rosemoor, near Great Torrington.
(a) When was this garden given to RHS? (b) By whom?

2 Where has a Millennium Garden been designed by Xa Tollemache?

3 Clovelly Court Garden has a particular specialism. What is it?

4 On the banks of the river Taw, the first Forestry Commission plantation in the UK was established in 1919 - where precisely?

5 When the Monkey Puzzle (*Araucaria araucana*) was introduced to Britain, one of the first specimens was planted at Pencarrow, Cornwall, in 1834, but the largest planting, forty trees, was the avenue to which estate in Devon?

6 Where atop Chit Rocks sit Connaught Gardens, renowned for floral displays, and named after the Duke who performed the opening ceremony in 1934?

7 Which gardens, in stream-fed lush seclusion, were created by the D'Oyly Carte family of Gilbert & Sullivan fame?

8 Which gardens provided the location for the filming of Jane Austen's *Sense and Sensibility*?

9 (a) Where is the National Collection of modern hybrid hostas?
(b) Where is the National Collection of oaks, with over 300 varieties?

10 What is the name of the secret garden in the heart of Tiverton at the rear of a Jacobean mansion?

11 What feature makes Garden House, Buckland Monachorum, well known?

12 Which garden has a collection of rare and exotic plants from around the world, has landscaped areas representing each of the five continents - the first of its kind - and maintains three NCCPG Primula Collections?

14 GEOGRAPHY AND GEOLOGY

Lundy HIGH, IT will be dry,
Lundy LOW, IT will be snow,
Lundy PLAIN, IT will be rain,
Lundy in HAZE, FINE for days.
Rhyme denoting Lundy's
role as a weather-vane.

The south wind blows and brings wet weather
The north gives wet and cold together
The west wind comes brimful of rain
The east wind drives it back again.
An old Dartmoor saying about
weather on the moor.

1 Which area has been designated an International Biosphere?

2 (a) How far from the mainland coast is Lundy Island?
(b) Renowned for spectacular diving and snorkelling, an area off Lundy has what particular clssification, one of only two in Britain?

3 Why are Kipling Tors at the back of Wesward Ho! so-named?

4 Where was the famous explorer Sir Francis Chichester born?

5 In which year was the terrible flood disaster which claimed the lives of thirty-five people, when after days of monsoon-like rain the swollen rivers of the East and West Lynn converged on stricken Lynmouth in a wall of water?

6 Although often referred to as Salcombe Estuary, and noted as such on Ordnance Survey maps, the waterway is not an estuary and no river drains into it. What is it?

7 In December 2001, the UN gave which spectacular stretch of coastline World Heritage status, the first natural site on mainland Britain to win the honour?

8 Okehampton is on the banks of which rivers?

9 The resort towns of Torquay, Paignton and Brixham together make up the English Riviera.
(a) How many miles of coastline are there on this Riviera?
(b) How many beaches and coves does this include?

10 What is geologically significant about Beer Head?

11 (a) Which is Devon's most southerly spot?
(b) What is the highest point between Exmoor and Dartmoor?

12 Where will you find both 'Rugged Jack' and 'White Lady'?

15 HOUSES

"And now the race is swept away   All to their dusty beds,
Still shall the mellow evening ray   Shine gaily on their heads,
While other faces fresh and new   Shall occupy the Squire's Pew."

Laura Jordan, relating the end of 800 years of continuous ownership of Holcombe Rogus Manor in 1858, when it was sold to pay gambling debts.

1 Sometimes known as 'The Little Versailles', Oldway Mansion at Paignton was built in 1874 for which industrial magnate?

2 Which house has associations with Shakespeare's 'Black Clifford', a Secret Treaty and a Cardinal's daughter?

3 Where is the 'Card House'?

4 Where can you learn to unravel the secret histories of sixteenth-century timber-framed buildings?

5 What is 'A La Ronde' in Summer Lane, Exmouth?

6 What is the name of the Victorian Gothic house at Bolham, two miles north of Tiverton, which has wonderful gardens and fascinating topiary?

7 Which is reputed to be the only haunted house where the ghost welcomes you?

8 How many properties does the National Trust maintain in Devon?

9 Which fortified house, one of few to survive, was home of Sir Humphrey Gilbert, founder of Newfoundland and half brother of Sir Walter Raleigh?

10 (a) Who in 1925 bought the run-down Dartington Estate and with vision and wealth began a project of rural regeneration which continues to this day?
(b) What is the name of the house on the estate which is a superb example of 1930s International Modernist architecture, and which now displays the Dartington Hall Trust Archive and collection of paintings and ceramics?

11 The great Victorian railway engineer Isambard Kingdom Brunel intended to retire to Torbay and designed a house for himself - where?

12 What, on 12 December 1961, happened to the Merchant's House in Edmund Street, Exeter?

16 INDUSTRY AND EMPLOYMENT

"*My sledge and hammer both declined*
My bellows too have lost their wind
My fire's extinct, my forge decayed
And in the dust, my vice is laid.
My coal is spent, my iron's gone
My nails are drove - my work is done."

Epitaph of 1820 to the village blacksmith in Meavy churchyard

1 Where is the Dartington Glass factory, where visitors can see glass being made?

2 Where is terra cotta pottery made in the traditional manner?

3 (a) Which town was famous for the manufacture of lace, examples of which can be seen in its Allhallows Museum?
(b) For which Queen's wedding dress was the lace made at Beer?
(c) Who first patented the machine which mechanised the manufacture of lace and where in Devon did he set up in production?

4 Where is the Clock Clinic, where famous faces are restored?

5 Which once-thriving nineteenth-century forge, powered by three water wheels, made tools for the local farming community and is now a museum?

6 Where is the home of Royal Barum Ware?

7 Where is water power being used to help reduce global warming?

8 Where is the last remaining oak bark tannery in the country?

9 The discovery of tin ore on Dartmoor caused a period of intense activity.
(a) Which were the four Stannary towns in Devon, where tinners went from the moorland mining areas to have their precious metal weighed, assayed, taxed and given the King's Stamp before it could be sold?
(b) What was the emblem adopted by tinners which can be seen in churches?

10 In what year did Thomas Whitty, an Axminster clothier, make his first carpet which was later to make the town's name a household word?

11 When was the last copper mine in Devon closed?

12 One of the world's largest operational china clay pits is in Devon. Where?

17 LITERATURE

Dear native brook! wild streamlet of the West!
Samuel Coleridge, *River Otter*, of his birthplace and boyhood

1 (a) Agatha Christie's novel *The Man in the Brown Suit* features Hempsley Cavern. On what was it modelled?
(b) Burgh Island, off the south Devon coast, has an *art deco* hotel where Agatha Christie often stayed and where she wrote which two books?

2 Bideford is associated with two famous authors
(a) Charles Kingsley lived here from 1854 and wrote which novel?
(b) Rudyard Kipling was educated at United Services College and based which book on his experiences there?

3 (a) The valleys of two Devon rivers, Torridge and Taw, are the main settings of *Tarka the Otter* by Henry Williamson. Where was Tarka born?
(b) Which other of his books is set in the same valleys?

4 What poem did Percy Bysshe Shelley write while living in Lynmouth during 1812-13?

5 Which novel did Evelyn Waugh write while staying at Easton Cross Hotel, Chagford?

6 Dartmoor is the setting for Sir Arthur Conan Doyle's most celebrated Sherlock Holmes story. What is it called?

7 *Lorna Doone*, published in 1869, is set on Exmoor. Who wrote it?

8 Which author lived from 1906 to 1924 at Wringstone Farm, Manaton, where he worked on many of his plays and novels, including *The Forsyte Saga*.

9 Which author has published more than sixty books, is a past winner of the Whitbread Award, and lives in Devon with his wife, both of whom have been awarded MBEs for their work for their charity *Farms for City Children*?

10 Beatrix Potter spent happy childhood holidays in Ilfracombe. Which of its features does she describe in one of her books?

11 Where was Sarah Catherine Martin living when she wrote the original *Mother Hubbard Nursery Rhymes*?

12 Charles Dickens, making the journey to Plymouth, became snowbound in South Zeal and wrote part of which novel in one of the inns here?

18 MISCELLANY

John Warren and Jone Cooke
But late they undertooke
Streat corners to sarch
Now baptised in Margery
The fruit of hys adultery
The 20 Daye of March.

In the parish register, Crediton, 1565

1 Joanna Southcott was a prophetess who had thousands of followers believing in her visions and religious claims. Where was she born, in June 1750?

2 North Devon is classified by the Council for the Protection of Rural England as one of only three areas in the country that can still be officially called ... what?

3 Where did Tom Pearce, of 'Uncle Tom Cobleigh' fame, stable his grey mare?

4 (a) What is the generic name given to people who live in Exeter?
(b) What was the Roman name of Exeter?
(c) What was Exeter called by the Saxons?

5 Dartmoor celebrated its 50th birthday as a National Park in 2001. Which two other centenaries were celebrated in that year, both concerned with Dartmoor?

6 Where is the annual World's Fireworks Championship held?

7 Where is the Britannia Royal Naval College, attended by both Prince Charles and Prince Andrew?

8 The Pepper Pot is a market building in which town?

9 Which four towns and villages featured in the BBC's series 'This Green and Pleasant Land', offering a taste of rural Devon as it is today?

10 A survey in 1995 by the Rural Development Commission showed that 41% of parishes had a church, 59% still had a shop - but how many had a pub?

11 (a) Where can you see the electrical re-juvenating machine?
(b) Where is the Norman Lockyer Observatory?

12 In which town is the Vistors' Centre located in a restored Southern Railway Station?

19 MUSEUMS AND HERITAGE

"See that ye hold fast the Heritage we leave you
Yea and teach your children to value that
never in the coming centuries their hearts
may fail them, or their hands grow weak."
Sir Francis Drake

1 Where is the Exmoor Brass Rubbing Centre?

2 Why is Bradninch included on the American Heritage Trail?

3 Where is a collection of British motorcycles and invacars displayed in an old world atmosphere?

4 Where can you see Moore's Patent Medical Machines, "... *improved pump for drawing the breasts of nurses, inhalers in metal for applying the vapour of vinegar, etc. to inflamed throats and ... wire leech appliers, medical spoons*"?

5 From which museum can you pick up a guide to 'Shipwreck Walks' and read about the tragic history behind the wrecks - some still visible?

6 Which are the two museums of the Two Museums Walk?

7 Where is the Centre of Playtime Doll and Toy Museum?

8 Where is the National Maritime Museum, a charity committed to conservation of the seas and life within them?

9 Where is maintained the world-famous 'Broughton Collection' of antique and modern glass paperweights?

10 Where is the Devonshire Collection of Period Costume?

11 Where is the oldest mass concrete bridge in the country?

12 Where was the world premiere of Gilbert and Sullivan's operetta *The Pirates of Penzance* performed in 1879?

20 MYTHS AND LEGENDS

> "*Take my drum to England, hang et by the shore,*
> *Strike et when your powder's runnin' low;*
> *If the Dons sight Devon, I'll quit the port o' Heaven,*
> *And drum them up the Channel as we drummed them long ago.*"
>
> Sir Henry Newboult's poem of 1897

1 Where is Drake's Drum, which legend says will sound to summon Sir Francis should England ever be in peril?

2 Who haunts the 'Spanish Barn' at Torre Abbey, Torquay?

3 Who sleeps at the Wibblestone on the beach at Appledore?

4 Why do unmarried ladies visit the Devonshire Inn at Sticklepath on New Year's Eve?

5 Which clock is reputed to have been the source of the nursery rhyme *Hickory Dickory Dock*?

6 Why don't the sow and piglets in the roof of St Brannock's church, Braunton, fly away?

7 Why do people travel from far and wide to see the spire of SS Peter and Paul's church, Ermington?

8 Why does the church at Buckfastleigh have over 100 steps leading up to its hilltop site?

9 Thomas Stuckley believed that cleanliness might spread infection: when he died in 1730 his house was filthy, with money piled in corners covered in dust and cobwebs. In which town did he live?

10 How did Spinsters' Rock at Drewsteignton, consisting of three uprights supporting a capstone built c.3500-2500 BC, but now denuded of the earth mound which covered it, get its name?

11 A large, holed boulder in the North Teign river on Dartmoor called Tolmen (*tol*=hole, *maen*=stone) has what particular curative value?

12 At a cross-roads in Manaton is a solitary grave, called Jay's Grave: why is it there?

21 POLITICAL AFFAIRS

Here lie I at the Chancel door,
Here lie I because I'm poor,
The further in the more you'll pay,
Here lie I as warm as they.

Epitaph at Kingsbridge, of "*Robert commonly called Bone Phillip*", who lived by charging a penny to be a scapegoat

1 Where can you see a collection of World War II fighting vehicles, guns, weapons and equipment in realistic settings?

2 Where was the birthplace of John Churchill, who was created the first Duke of Marlborough after the battle of Blenheim?

3 (a) On which Devon beach were the D-Day landings rehearsed?
(b) A simple obelisk on the edge of Slapton Sands pays tribute to what?
(c) What reminder of this event can be seen at Torcross?

4 Where did a bullet whistle through the nursery window where the baby Princess (later Queen) Victoria lay sleeping?

5 What is the connection between Hatherleigh and the Crimean War?

6 Where can you see the graves of three English Rajahs of Sarawak?

7 Where can you see an example of 'Palmerston's follies'?

8 A wealthy family, the Champernownes of Modbury gained power in the courts of Henry VIII and Elizabeth I. Katherine Champernowne was the mother of three notable Elizabethans - who were they?

9 Devon boasts both the oldest and the second oldest boroughs in England. Name both.

10 Why is Wolford chapel, near Honiton, owned by the State of Ontario, Canada?

11 (a) Where did Prince William of Orange land in 1688 in his successful 'Glorious Revolution' to oust James II from the throne?
(b) How many people have since stood on the stone he disembarked onto?

12 There is a statue of Francis Drake overlooking the canal in Tavistock and one on Plymouth Hoe. Which is the original and which is the copy?

22 PUBS

Taverns and ordinaries
Were his chiefest braveries,
Golden angels there flew up and down;
Riots were his best delights
With stately feasting day and night,
In court and city thus he won renown.

Contemporary ballad to the courtier and rake Captain 'Lusty' Stucley, who was born *c.*1532 at West Worlington, Chulmleigh.

1 Which was England's first hotel, and has a connection with Russian royals?

2 How did Smokey House Inn, Marldon, get its name?

3 Tally Ho Country Inn at Hatherleigh serves 'Potboilers Brew'. What is it named after?

4 (a) In which inn, regarded as the most solitary in Devon, has the roaring fire in the bar been kept burning for over a hundred years?
(b) Why does this inn stand on this particular side of the road on land belonging to the Duchy of Cornwall?

5 (a) What is the name of the pub on Burgh Island, in Bigbury Bay?
(b) When was the pub built?
(c) How far, according to the finger post, is Burgh Island from England?

6 What is The Beer Engine, in Exeter?

7 Where is the oldest 'White Hart' pub in the country?

8 Which is Devon's southern-most hotel?

9 Where is The Cherub?

10 Torrington Railway Station has been transformed into a pub. What is its name?

11 Where is Nobody Inn?

12 Which pub in Exeter is named after the patron saint of woolcombers?

23 RECORD BREAKERS

"He departed this life Nov. 14 1802 Aged 57
Wound up
In hopes of being taken in hand
By his Maker
And of being thoroughly cleaned, repaired
And set-going
In the world to come."

Punning epitaph to "*the outsize case of George Routledge, watchmaker ... Integrity was the mainspring, and prudence the regulator of all the actions of his life*", Lydford churchyard.

1 Which is the only town or village in Britain with an exclamation mark as part of its name?

2 Which is Devon's oldest holiday resort?

3 Where is Squeezebelly Passage, the narrowest in Devon?

4 Which lighthouse is, paradoxically, the highest but shortest in England?

5 Which and where is the narrowest street in Britain and which even claims to be the 'narrowest street in the world'

6 Where will you find the longest village street in Britain?

7 Which beach is uniquely formed of sea shells which have been carried by the Gulf Stream from the tropical waters of the Caribbean?

8 Which was the last castle to be built in England?

9 Where, according to the *Guinness Book of World Record Breakers*, will you find the largest collection of garden gnomes in the world?

10 Which is Devon's most southerly resort?

11 According to the *Guinness Book of Records*, where was the world's biggest bonfire held?

12 Which is England's highest waterfall?

24 SAINTS AND SINNERS

"It is my belief, Watson, founded upon my experience, that the lowest and vilest alleys in London do not present a more dreadful record sin than does the smiling and beautiful countryside ...Think of the deeds of hellish cruelty, the hidden wickedness which may go on, year in year out, in such places, and none the wiser."
Arthur Conan Doyle, *The Hound of the Baskervilles*

1 In which 'town' is Dartmoor Prison situated? Who owns Dartmoor Prison?

2 Where was Ffyona Campbell, the first woman to claim that she walked around the world, born?

3 Who was 'Resurrection Bob'?

4 (a) Where is Betsy Grimbal's Tower? (b) Who loved Betsy Grimbal?

5 In which Devon town, *c*.680 AD, was St Boniface born and is celebrated?

6 At Dartmouth Castle it is possible to explore the fourteenth-century ruins of Hawley's Fortalice. (a) Who was Hawley?
(b) For which literary figure was he the inspiration?

7 In what way was the Dartmoor Inn, at the junction of the A386 in Lydford, made famous in Charles Kingsley's *Westward Ho!*?

8 (a) Lydford Castle was not built as a castle - why was it built?
(b) How did the rhyme arise: "*Hast ever hear of Lydford law -*
How in the morn they hang and draw
and sit in judgment after?"

9 Stocks are a not uncommon village feature, but what rarer form of punishment can you find in Hemyock Castle?

10 Who was 'the man they couldn't hang' at Exeter Gaol, and what happened to him?

11 Why is the folly on the far side of Wringcliff Bay, Valley of Rocks, Lynton, called Jennifred's Leap?

12 Who is it suggested was the model for the wicked squire in Conan Doyle's novel *The Hound of the Baskervilles*?

25 SPORT

In speechless
Silence my youthful
Daye soon sped I
Left my cradle and
Come here to bed.

Epitaph for Richard Downe, died 1710, at Exbourne

1 When and where is the Grizzly Run, Europe's most popular multi-terrain race?

2 (a) The golf course at Saunton is classified as what?
(b) Which is the country's oldest golf links?

3 (a) What is The Smugglers Trail? (b) What is the Buzzard Route?

4 Where can you get carriage driving lessons?

5 (a) How long is the East Devon Way?
(b) What is its logo?

6 Which golf club is situated in an internationally renowned wildlife conservation area with fantastic sea and estuary views and has won an award for its excellent condition?

7 (a) There are two National Hunt Racing courses in Devon - name them both.
(b) Which horse race, initiated in the 1950s and now run annually in October, brings to mind one of the interests of the famous writer Agatha Christie?

8 Which tennis player was known locally when young as the 'Paignton Peach', became internationally famous, and then went on to create a career as a TV sports commentator and quiz presenter?

9 Where is the River Dart Raft Race held, annually in October?

10 What is the name given to (a) Exeter Football Club?
(b) Exeter Rugby Union Football Club?

11 Where are the UK National Tug of War Championships held?

12 On a particular week-end in the middle of May, upwards of 2,000 youngsters converge on Dartmoor for an event organised by the Army: what?

26 TOWNS AND CITIES

Ill fares the land, to hastening ills a prey;
Where wealth accumulates, and men decay.

Oliver Goldsmith, *The Deserted Village*

1 Agatha Christie, the most published mystery writer of all time with 79 crime novels and many plays to her name, was born in which town?

2 Which town has a bronze town map created by local children with sculptor Roger Dean, and works of art - a carved bridge, seats, murals - placed around it all produced by local people?

3 Why was the town of Salcombe previously known as Saltcombehaven?

4 Where was Captain Robert F Scott of the Antarctic born?

5 A unique cliff railway carries passengers and freight up and down the steep valley wall between Lynton and Lynmouth.
(a) When was it built? (b) How is it powered?

6 Where was the birthplace in 1791 of Charles Babbage who designed 'calculating engines' which were the forerunners of the modern computer?.

7 Exeter's Guildhall is one of England's oldest municipal buildings, and next door is the Turks Head Inn: of which famous author was this a favourite haunt?

8 Name Plymouth's four town gates (as depicted in the city's coat of arms).

9 Towns such as Dartmouth, Totnes and Kingsbridge have their 'Shambles' - open-fronted colonnaded buildings where traders set up stalls to sell meat, fish and farm produce. In what way is the 'Shambles' at Uffculme different?

10 (a) Where are the only subterranean medieval vaulted passages which are open to the public?
(b) Why were they constructed?

11 The palm tree serves as part of the logo for the towns comprising the English Riviera. Why?

12 Which is the largest town within the Dartmoor National Park?

27 TRANSPORT AND COMMUNICATION

To win a husband long she tried,
Nor in despair at last she died;
She heard that marriages were made
In heaven, so this world she bade
Goodbye, to try, since hopeless here,
Her fortune in another sphere.
Epitaph for an old maid

Here lie I, and no wonder
I'm dead
For a wagon wheel
ran over my head
In memory of Thomas Snell, in a North Devon churchyard

1 What is the name given to the A39 after it leaves Bideford and goes south to Wadebridge in Cornwall?

2 (a) What is the Tarka Line?
(b) Why do all trains on this line stop at Eggesford?

3 What is the name of the 100-foot historic three-masted schooner whose restoration was completed in 2001at Bideford Quay, but could not clear out of the Torridge River because her restored masts were found to be too tall?

4 What has been described as 'the most scenic tramway in Britain' runs from Seaton
(a) to where?
(b) what is the gauge of the tramline?
(c) how long has it been running on this site?

5 Name the two regional airports in Devon.

6 Isambard Kingdom Brunel commissioned an 'atmospheric railway' in Devon.
(a) How was it powered? (b) Where did it run to and from?

7 How many arches does Barnstaple's Long Bridge have spanning the river Taw?

8 Which charity holds Thomas the Tank Engine events every summer?

9 Where is the 'Station that time forgot', where you can ride on two different railways?

10 Where is the eighteenth-century toll house which displays the charges of 1d for a pedestrian, 2d for a bullock, 5d for a horse and cart and 1s for a coach?

11 Where is the only Grade II Listed signal box in the country?

12 What is the name of the ship which makes day trips to Lundy Island from Bideford and Ilfracombe?

28 VILLAGES

Neglected by his doctor
Ill-treated by his nurse
His brother robbed the widow
Which made the matter worse

Epitaph formerly in a North Devon churchyard

1 (a) In which village is the cobbled main street of Up-a-long/Down-a-long?
(b) Many of the cottages bear the initials 'C.H.' and a date - why?

2 The main street of this village winds along the valley, or combe, for more than two miles, and is reputedly one of the longest in the country. Which?

3 (a) How is the name of the village of Dittisham pronounced?
(b) How is Woolfardisworthy pronounced?

4 What was the name given by Victorian tourists to the Lynton-Lynmouth area?

5 In which village will you find one of the oldest churches in England, with a complete Saxon crypt?

6 In what way are Mary Tavy and Peter Tavy related?

7 Which is the highest village on Dartmoor?

8 In which village was Charles Kingsley, author of *Westward Ho!* and *The Water Babies,* born?

9 Slapton Sands is renowned for the part it played in the 'rehearsals' for the D-Day landings. At the northern end of the beach, in the cliff face, some joist holes and the remains of a wall are all that are left of a village. What was the village and why did it disappear?

10 What can be seen growing from the masonry at the top of All Saints church tower, Culmstock, and was mentioned by R D Blackmore in his romantic novel *Perlycross*, making it at least 200 years old?

11 Which village is world famous for the type and quality of the thatch on almost every cottage?

12 What are the 'Alphabet Parishes of North Devon'?

ANSWERS

1 ANIMALS

1 The Exmoor Zoological Park, which has over 150 species of wildlife.
2 Holsworthy, where fairs and markets have been held for over 700 years.
3 Timothy, soon to celebrate his 160th birthday, who lives in the rose garden. Captured in 1854 from Portuguese brigands by Captain John Courtenay Everard, a relative of the 10th Earl of Devon, he saw service aboard ships in the Crimea, the East Indies and the South China Sea until given permanent home leave in 1892 and handed to the Devon family. He has outlived seven Earls and in 1926 was found to be female!
4 Very sure-footed, horned, feral but docile goats, which are found nowhere else on Exmoor.
5 April
6 (a) The wild red deer; the Scottish Islands also have a population. They are a direct descendant of the wild deer which roamed the Exmoor forests in prehistoric times.
(b) Between 800 and 1,000
(c) The 'head' is the name given to the stag's elaborate growth of antler, the glory of this animal. By the time a stag is 8 years old it should have 3 points, 'brow, bay and trey', on each main stem or 'beam' of the horn.
(d) The noise is called 'belling'.
7 At the Hedgehog Hospital, Prickly Ball Farm, Newton Abbot.
8 At Sidmouth, where it was founded by Dr Elizabeth Svendsen.
9 To Paignton Zoo, which had opened in 1923, and now has over 1,000 animals with 60 endangered species; it was the location for the BBC TV's *Zookeeper* series.
10 (a) The Centre is based at Yealmpton (b) King is the world's tallest horse.
11 Known as the 'hunting parson', John Russell (1795-1883) was born in Dartmouth, and from 1830 to 1880 was perpetual curate of Swymbridge near Barnstaple, where he became Master of Foxhounds. He developed the West Country terrier named the 'Jack Russell' after him, a dog able to keep up with the horses, small enough to follow the fox through narrow crevices and not so aggressive that it would kill the fox.
12 Devon Red Ruby Cattle.

2 ARCHAEOLOGY

1 The Nine Stones circle is high on windswept Belstone Tor, Dartmoor, where according to some people the maidens still dance daily at noon.
2 The standing stone, made of slate and very thin if looked at from the side, is 9 feet (nearly 3 m) tall. Some people say it is a fertility menhir or has curative powers.
3 The hills nearby are called Great Hangman and Little Hangman, but there is no evidence that they were sites of executions. The name of the stone derives from the Saxon 'stanes hengen', meaning hanging or uplifting stones. There is however folklore that a thief stole a sheep and tied it round his neck to make it easier for him to carry home, but as the animal soon became heavy he rested on a rock where unfortunately for him the sheep struggled, slid over the other side of the stone and strangled him.
4 Durotriges and Dumnonii
5 Shoulsbury (or Shoulsbarrow) Castle
6 The Fosse Way - not so named by the Romans but by the later Saxons, for whom a *fosse* was a ditch at the side of the road.
7 Kents Cavern, at Babbacombe, Torquay.
8 The Brutus Stone is at Totnes, where the Mayor stands to announce the accession of a monarch. It is supposed to mark the spot where Brutus the Trojan set foot when he colonised Britain, but its name is more likely to be derived from 'Bruiter's Stone', used for proclamations (from the French *bruire*, to sound).
9 The Falklands War Memorial at Fort Stanley.

10 It is the most complete Bronze Age village site in England, with a circular wall 10 feet (3m) thick and 6 feet (2m) tall enclosing 4 acres (1.6 ha) of ground and with a stream diverted to pass within the pound wall. The 16 round huts for human occupation had hearths and sleeping benches, with a further 6 for storage and 4 for cattle pens.
11 In the garden of Six Acre Farm, Lynton.
12 A ring of Iron Age hill forts encircling the western approaches of Dartmoor.

3 ART AND THE ARTS

1 Broomhill Sculpture Gardens and Art Gallery, and Dewsmoor Art near Crediton.
2 On the beach of Budleigh Salterton; it depicts the young Raleigh listening with rapt attention to daring tales of the sea told by an old 'salt'. The low curving wall by which the seaman is sitting is still here, as is Octagon House on the sea front, in which Millais rented a room. Millais composed his masterpiece by the old sea wall before finishing it in his London studio.
3 Plymouth
4 Chagford
5 Saltram, Plympton
6 Samuel Palmer painted 'The Lonely Tower' when he visited the area in 1835.
7 The rock, with its unusual formation, is on the beach at Thurlestone.
8 The Cardew Teapottery, Bovey Tracey, home of the world's most extraordinary teapots.
9 The Festival is held in Sidmouth over eight days at the beginning of August. Considered the country's best folk festival, it has over 600 acts from around the world.
10 The area is a down-town melange of music, arts and street craft.
11 The bridge over the River Axe at Bickleigh.
12 Sir Joshua Reynolds (1723-92), who was buried in St Paul's.

4 BIRDS AND BEASTS

1 The Wildlife and Dinosaur Park is in Combe Martin
2 At West Putford, Bradworthy, where you will meet more than 1,000 Gnomes (and also Pixies) set in woodland and wild flower gardens. The Gnome Garden was entered for the Turner Art Prize, but was not successful. Ann Atkin, the artist-owner, organises International Gnome Days.
3 Quince Honey Farm, South Molton
4 The RSPB's nature reserve at Aylesbeare Common.
5 Bowling Green Marsh and Exminster Marsh, which are coastal grazing marshes supporting redwings, curlews, lapwings and widgeons.
6 Avocet Cruises
7 It is held in Exeter, normally in May of each year.
8 Worms are charmed in Dartmouth, in May of each year.
9 At Saker Falconry, a bird of prey centre which also displays owls, hawks and vultures.
10 George Montague arrived in Kingsbridge in 1798 with Eliza Dorville, his 'friend in science' and mistress, and was the first to describe the ashy coloured falcon now known as Montague's harrier, which he found nesting on a hillside nearby. However, it is the cirl bunting that links him to this area, which he found in Tacket Wood, just outside Kingsbridge: although they were known on the continent, no-one had identified them in Britain before. Eliza engraved a drawing of the bird for Montague's *Ornithological Dictionary*, published in in 1802.
11 The buzzard.
12 On a National Trust site on Dartmoor.

5 CASTLES

1 Watermouth Castle which is situated between Ilfracombe and Combe Martin.

2 Compton Castle, four miles west of Torquay, was built at three periods 1340, 1450 and 1520 by the Gilbert family, who still live here.

3 Bickleigh Castle

4 (a) Berry Pomeroy, between Totnes and Paignton, which is shrouded in sinister folklore and legend, with tales of apparitions and kidnappings.

(b) The Pomeroy and Seymour families each left a legacy of their occupation, the great gatehouse of the Pomeroys and the impressive stone mansion of the Seymours.

5 A young Courtenay woman, celebrating her marriage with a game of hide and seek, climbed into a large chest, and was never seen again. Opened many years later, the chest revealed a skeleton and a yellowing dress! Some say she still haunts the grounds ...

6 (a) Castle Drogo is one of the most remarkable works of the architect Sir Edwin Lutyens

(b) Born in 1856, Julius Drew (he added the final 'e' in 1910) was the son of a Bedfordshire vicar with family connections in the tea trade. In 1883, he opened a shop in London and began the Home & Colonial grocery chain, which by 1890 had grown to 107 shops throughout Britain. Interested in his ancestry, he met a Drewe family near Honiton and from this contrived his descent from a Baron Dru, who had come to England with William the Conqueror, and whose family had given its name to Drewsteignton. He then surmised himself to be the descendant of the Norman Baron Drogo de Teign. The scene was set for Castle Drogo.

7 It was built originally during the fifteenth century, when it was then one of the most advanced fortresses of its day, positioned to protect the homes and warehouses of Dartmouth's wealthy medieval merchants.

8 (a) Haldon Belvedere

(b) It is a triangular folly, standing 900 feet above sea level on the Haldon Hills, Dunchideock, built by an ex-Governor of Madras.

9 Since 1391 the western bank of the Exe estuary has been guarded by magnificent medieval Powderham Castle. Built by Sir Philip Courtenay, it remains the home of the Courtenay family, Earls of Devon.

10 The 'Two Castles Trail' is a twenty-four mile walk between the two Norman castles of Okehampton and Launceston (just over the border in Cornwall).

11 Both are owned by Sir Hugh Stucley, 6th Baronet, who lives at the Castle. Hartland Abbey was the last monastery to be dissolved by Henry VIII. Legend has it that Henry Abbott, Keeper of the King's Wine Cellar, won the Abbey from him in a game of tennis.

12 It continues to be used as a prison.

6 CHURCHES

1 Exeter cathedral, where the beautifully carved oak Bishop's Throne soars to over twenty metres, rising almost to the vaulting, and constructed without a single nail.

2 (a) Buckfast Abbey, Buckfastleigh, where there is also a 'Physic Garden' based on evidence of plants which were being used before 1539, a 'Sensory Garden' and a 'Lavender Garden', which contains the National Collection.

(b) Founded in 1018 by Aethelweard, an earl under King Canute, under the Benedictine Rule, it became a Cistercian monastery in 1148 but was closed in 1539 by Henry VIII, when it became home to Sir Richard Grenville and later Sir Francis Drake. It then lay in ruins until Benedictine monks returned in 1882. The Abbey Church was rebuilt on its medieval foundations, and was completed in 1938; astonishingly, it represents thirty-two years of labour by just four monks.

3 It reads 'MY DEAR MOTHER'; the local lord of the manor, William Whitley, had it painted in 1928.

4 The notice is on display at Molland church, where there is an ornate three-tier pulpit, pews of varying heights - and the walls lean outwards at startling angles.

5 The pew-ends in All Saints church, East Budleigh, relate to the trades of the pews' original occupants, providing an insight into life at the time.

6 The Quakers of Sticklepath were the first people in Devon to welcome John Wesley. The white-painted rock is the one on which he stood to preach.

7 (a) The magnificent church at Widecombe, seen long before the village is reached.

(b) The church was struck by a thunderbolt during divine service on Sunday, 21 October 1638, when a pinnacle was knocked off the tower and fell through the roof killing four worshippers and injuring many more - a contemporary record claims they were killed by a 'fiery ball' passing through the church: was this an example of ball lightning? Legend claims that Jan Reynolds, a local man, had borrowed money from the Devil to pay gambling debts and was due to repay it on that Sunday. Finding Jan in church, the Devil hauled him out and as the pair flew into the air a trailing foot (or cloven hoof) dislodged the pinnacle.

8 In 1821, twelve-year-old John Beasley built a miniature replica at Rock, half a mile away from the parish church, 12 feet 9 inches long, 3 feet 9 inches wide and 14 feet high, complete with gargoyles and a weather-vane.

9 The clock in the church at Ottery St Mary was made between 1327 and 1369 on the principle that the earth was the centre of the universe, and shows the 24-hour day and the phases of the moon.

10 (a) '*Abide With Me*' (b) Toplady was incumbent of Harpford for some time.

11 Completed only in 1963, the design of the church came to the vicar, Revd William Keble Martin, in a dream so vivid that he sketched it over breakfast. It has no chancel but three naves radiating from a sanctuary, and is 1000 inches long, 1000 inches broad and 1000 inches high.

12 (a) The earliest work, the transepts and transeptal towers, are of *c.*1170.
(b) Great Peter, which at over six tons is one of Britain's largest bells.

7 CUSTOMS

1 Barnstaple, Bideford, South Molton, Torrington. The name derives from the traditional way in which people carried their produce to market in large baskets or 'panniers'.

2 Hunting of the Earl of Rone

3 (a) Westward Ho! (b) The first week in August.

4 Shaldon

5 (a) For traders of old, payment of money on the mushroom-shaped stone in the Merchants' Exchange sealed a bargain: the placing of hands and money on the stone was taken traditionally as a symbol of good faith and integrity.
(b) It is a large white glove garlanded with flowers and set on a long pole, pushed out of the top window of the Guildhall to greet all the visitors.

6 It is held annually on the second Tuesday in September.

7 (a) At Morchard Bishop, where a huge effigy of a ghostly hound is carried four miles through the lanes he is supposed to haunt, accompanied by crowds singing, dancing and waving lanterns. There is a hamlet nearby called Black Dog.
(b) Annually on the first Saturday of October

8 (a) The ceremony is held at Ottery St Mary on 5 November. Young men, their hands and arms swathed in sacking, take turns to run through the streets carrying nine blazing barrels containing burning tar. 'Pixie Day' is in June, when local children dress as pixies, try to capture the church bell-ringers and regain control of the town.
(b) On the second Saturday in November, Hatherleigh Carnival involves a sleigh, alight with burning tar barrels, being dragged through the streets.

9 (a) At Modbury, whose Charter dates from 1310, the start is indicated by the Town Crier hoisting a glove and flowers as a symbol of free trade.
(b) Once, anyone could sell liquor exempt from duty during the fair provided that a holly bush was hung outside the premises.
(c) At Honiton, the fair in July starts with a gilded glove hoisted on a pole outside the New Dolphin pub and hot coppers are thrown for 'poor' children to scramble for.

10 They are held at Ashburton ; the annual medieval fair is held in July.

11 At Shebbear, 'Turning the Devil's Boulder' dates to before the time of Guy Fawkes. The massive, squat stone lying outside the churchyard was dropped by the Devil on his way to harm the village, and is turned by the villagers each November 5, after a deliberately discordant peal of bells is rung to frighten Old Nick away. If the stone is not turned, the village will have bad luck.

12 Visitors started to come to Dartmoor after the railway reached Exeter in 1844. In 1854 the guide John Perrott of Chagford originated 'Dartmoor letter boxes' by leaving tourists' visiting cards in a cairn, with a glass jar inside, at Cranmere Pool. There are now many boxes scattered about the moor and Letterboxing has become a sport directed by the Dartmoor 100 Club: authorised boxes have stamps

which the letterboxer can use to mark his/her own record sheet. Collectors of 100 stamps qualify to join the club.

8 DARTMOOR

1 365 square miles, at 23 miles wide in its northern half and 24 miles from north to south.
2 The highest point is High Willhays, at 2,038 feet; the second highest point is Yes Tor (2029 feet); they are the highest ground in England south of the Pennines.
3 The Meeting is held at Modbury, annually in April.
4 (a) At any one time approximately 3,000 ponies live in the National Park; this compares with 30,000 roaming wild on Dartmoor in 1950.
(b) The ponies, each with a distinctive ear or tail mark, are not truly wild but are owned by farmers, known as Commoners who have a traditional right to let their livestock graze on Dartmoor. The ponies are unbroken, coming into contact with their owners only at the 'drifts' (round-ups) each summer.
(c) Dartmoor Commoners Council.
5 It is both an Area of Outstanding Natural Beauty and a Site of Special Scientific Interest, designations given because of the wide diversity of plant and animal life which thrive in the moist sheltered atmosphere of the secluded valley.
6 It is where the East and West branches of the River Dart meet in a wooded valley.
7 Bowerman's Nose is a 20 feet (6m) high natural stack of granite, on Hayne Down. A strange tor unmistakable for its likeness to a human caricature, in legend it immortalises a man who hunted on the Sabbath and was turned into stone for his sins.
8 Postbridge, on the East Dart River, half way between Tavistock and Moretonhampstead.
9 Okehampton Range, Merrivale Range and Willsworthy Range, which together use about 15% of the National Park's area. There has been military training on Dartmoor since 1873, and in 1991 the Duchy of Cornwall allowed MOD a further 21-year lease.
10 (a) London Bridge (the foundation stone from Haytor was laid in 1825), Nelson's Column, Holborn Viaduct, New Scotland Yard and the British Museum. You can still see the stone sets of the earliest horse-drawn tramway, with a gauge of 4 feet, built by George Templer in 1820 to take stone from his quarries at Haytor to a canal at Bovey Tracey and hence by barge to Teignmouth for onward shipping .
(b) Merrivale Quarry ceased production in 1998.
11 The word uses exactly half of the alphabet, using each letter once!
12 The oak is on the green at Meavy, reputedly 800 years old.

9 EXMOOR

1 (a) The boundaries were laid down in 1954 under the National Parks and Access to Countryside Act of 1949. The area is 268 square miles (694 sq km), making it the second smallest National Park in England and Wales.
(b) A majestic head of a ten-pointer red stag in black on a green triangle.
2 Two
3 The wall was 29 miles (46km) long. They also built 22 miles (35km) of public roads connecting Simonsbath, at the heart of Exmoor, to the outside world.
4 It comes from 'hlynn', meaning a torrent, very appropriate for the East and West Lyn Rivers which give their names to the two towns still remembered for the flood tragedy of the summer of 1952, when 300 million gallons of rain fell within five hours on The Chains, a marshy watershed above the towns.
5 Mother Melldrum was the old soothsayer and wise woman of R D Blackmore's *Lorna Doone*. Her 'kitchen' is in the Cheesewring area in the Valley of Rocks. Castle Rock, the most prominent feature, has a 400-foot drop on its seaward side, and was the home of Aggie Norman, a mad woman whom Blackmore is thought to have made into Mother Melldrum in his novel.
6 Combe Martin, with seaside surroundings close to the Hangman Hills.
7 The Barle, which rises in The Chains and eventually joins the Exe some two miles (3km) below Dulverton on Exmoor's southern boundary.

8 At 1,059 feet, County Gate is the meeting place of Devon and Somerset.

9 (a) The sturdy, agile creatures stand at 12 hands, which corresponds closely with wild horse skeletons found in prehistoric deposits.

(b) The distinguishing features are its mealy muzzle and eye-cingle.

(c) 1921

10 Exmoor Horn Sheep

11 In the nineteenth century, Fanny Pope kept an inn at Heath Poult Cross. She would frequently turn herself into a hare to give the harriers their fun and then resume her human form and her occupation of selling beer.

12 Bogs fed by the heavy rains (70 inches or more annually) on the flattish summits.

10 FILM AND TV

1 Mothecombe

2 Axminster and Bampton

3 *Hornblower*

4 In the countryside around Exeter

5 Oldway Mansion, Paignton

6 (a) Paignton and Dartmouth Railway (b) Burgh Island

7 Saunton Sands

8 Bayard's Cove, near Dartmouth.

9 Saltram House, at Plympton, Plymouth.

10 The Quayside, Exeter, which is again becoming an important aspect of Exeter's life.

11 Staverton station, which is everyone's image of a between-the-wars rural branch line station. Volunteers of the South Devon Railway have restored it.

12 It is Rushford Tower near Chagford, a small, square folly, from the top of which is an excellent view of Castle Drogo.

11 ALL AT SEA

1 Start Point, where the clifftop lighthouse warns shipping of the treacherous Blackstone Rock; Berry Head, Brixham; Hartland Lighthouse; Eddystone Lighthouse, off Plymouth Sound, the fourth building here, now with a candlepower of 570,000 (the first lighthouse of 1698 had a beam of 24 candles); a smaller lighthouse stands at the western end of the Breakwater, built to protect Plymouth Sound from the gales that used to ravage the harbour; Bull Point, built in 1879 to warn vessels of the grievous Morte Stone reef; Lundy North Light which is no longer staffed but controlled by South Light near the Landing Beach; Lundy; Ilfracombe, where the thirteenth-century lighthouse and chapel has been guarding the harbour for six hundred years; Foreland Point.

2 It was one of the locations used for filmimg *The French Lieutenant's Woman*.

3 It commemorates Elizabeth I's patronage of West Teignmouth.

4 They are former World War II Royal Navy Torpedo boats.

5 (a) *Mayflower* and *Speedwell*

(b) It put into Bayards Cove, Dartmouth, as it had sprung a leak even before leaving the Devon coast - its a tricky business discovering new worlds.

6 Totnes. It was big enough to fill Centre Court at Wimbledon, and designed to crest the waves at 40 knots, but ran into trouble on both its sea trials.

7 It shines a beacon at night to guide shipping in the Bristol Channel.

8 On the night of 12 January 1899 the *Forest Hall* was foundering off the North Devon coast. The seas were too rough for the Lynmouth lifeboat *Louisa* to be launched so the crew agreed that the only way to go in rescue was to carry it 15 miles up Countisbury Hill and down Porlock Hill, to Porlock where the waters were calmer. The *Louisa* was eventually launched at 8am, but the men found the strength to row through the gale force winds and storm-lashed waves to the *Forest Hall*. The ship's rudder was smashed, but she had got both anchors down and was being helped by the tug *Joliffe* which had been

standing by all night! The danger which the Lynmouth men feared did not exist.
The exhausted lifeboatmen returned, many hours later, to the *Louisa's* home port. They had done their duty and expected no reward, but each received an extra £5 - then had to pay for repairs to a cottage wall on the last bend of the twisting Porlock Hill, damaged in their dramatic struggle to get the lifeboat to Porlock: this would have left them out of pocket had not the grateful owners of the *Forest Hall* contributed £75.

9 (a) Plymouth, Salcombe, Torbay, Teignmouth and Exmouth along the south coast; Clovelly, Appledore and Ilfracombe on the north coast.
(b) Exmouth and Plymouth were both established in 1803.
10 The trawler race is held in the port of Brixham.
11 The Royal Regatta takes place in Torbay.
12 It is moored in Brixham harbour.

12 FOOD AND DRINK

1 East of the A388, south of Clawton
2 Dartmouth
3 (a) Sherford - the secret of real Devon cider. (b) Lyme Bay Winery, Axminster
4 They are varieties of cheese. Hunting Pink is a semi-hard cheese flavoured with pink peppercorns, made to an old Devon recipe.
5 Paignton and Dartmouth
6 The 200 year old Plymouth Gin was reputedly a favourite of Winston Churchill.
7 Genuine Devon-made ice cream
8 Proper Job Cooperative
9 For eating - particularly with bacon and egg on top.
10 Pasteurised ewes' milk products including hard and soft cheeses, ice cream and fudge.
11 The first Balti house to open here was the Ma Ha - Bha Rat in Kingsbridge.
12 'Two point five four centimetres Cider'

13 GARDENS AND PLANTS

1 RHS Garden Rosemoor is a 40-acre garden of national importance.
(a) 1988 (b) Lady Anne Palmer
2 Castle Hill, Filleigh, home of Lord and Lady Arran.
3 A restored Victorian kitchen garden.
4 Eggesford Forest has the distinction of being the first Forestry Commission plantation in the UK. By the end of the First World War many thousands of acres of native forests had been destroyed and this marked the first step to redress the balance.
5 Bicton House, East Budleigh. Lord Rolle, who according to his epitaph was "*the last representative of one of the most ancient and opulent families in Devon*", had the formal gardens laid out in grand style and rare trees were introduced from all over the world. Bicton is a Grade I listed park and garden. The avenue of 'monkey puzzle' trees is particularly famous. The name is said to have been given when someone looked at the rough spiky trunk and remarked that it would puzzle even a monkey to climb it.
6 Sidmouth - the event is recorded on a plaque on the rear wall of the terrace.
7 Coleton Fishacre
8 Flete Manor, near Ivybridge; the cottage on the estate became home to the Dashwood family.
9 (a) Sticklepath (b) Chevithorne Barton, near Tiverton.
10 The Great House Garden
11 Its romantic walled garden - but is also has a Cretan and an Italian garden.
12 Plant World, a unique plantsman's garden between Torquay and Newton Abbot.

14 GEOGRAPHY AND GEOLOGY

1 Braunton Burrows, one of the largest sand dune systems in the UK and now designated of international importance - one of only three such in the country.

2 (a) The Island, 3 miles long and half-a-mile wide, is twelve miles from the mainland.
(b) It is a Marine Nature Reserve - the other is around the Isle of Skoma.

3 Rudyard Kipling went to school here and the Tors take his name.

4 He was born in the village of Shirwell, just outside Barnstaple.

5 By late afternoon on 15 August, 1952, the sky had turned black over the slopes of Exmoor. Leaden clouds plunged Lynmouth into an eerie half-light. That day saw one of the heaviest falls of rain recorded in Britain - 9.1 inches. Most of it fell on The Chains above the town, and soon the moorland streams became raging torrents. Water and rock crashed towards the coast, an estimated 90 million tons in all. By the time the deluge hit Lynmouth's narrow streets it had become a wall of water at least 12 feet high. The homes of nearly 1,000 resuidents were wrecked. The High Street was littered with boulders piled 20 feet high.

6 It is a ria, or drowned valley, so the salinity is undiluted.

7 The 95 miles of 'Jurassic Coast' reaches from Studland Bay in Dorset to Orccombe Point, Exmouth - a significant proportion in Devon.

8 The Rivers East and West Okement, which meet where Okehampton is sited; they are the only Dartmoor rivers to head north, to the Bristol Channel.

9 (a) 22 miles of coastline (b) 18 beaches and coves - Paignton has the longest beach.

10 It is the last outcrop, furthest west of southern England's chalk.

11 (a) Prawle Point (b) Stoodleigh Beacon, at 978 feet above sea level.

12 In the Valley of Rocks, where mysterious-looking weathered rock formations have their own stories with appropriate names. The Valley is thought to have been the original bed of the River Lyn before it diverted course to break through to the sea at Lynmouth.

15 HOUSES

1 Isaac Singer, the sewing machine magnate. Isaac Singer's original mansion was a yellow-brick villa and owes much of its Neo-classical appearance to a 1904 restoration by his son, Paris, into a style more associated with Versailles than with seaside Devon, with a sweeping Italianate marble staircase and a gallery of mirrors. Paris lived here with his mistress, the American dancer Isadora Duncan.

2 Ugbrooke House, ancestral home of the Lords Clifford of Chudleigh. The original house and church were built *c.* 1200 and but later redesigned by Robert Adam.

3 The Card House, now the 'Pack O' Cards' pub, is in the main street at Combe Martin. It was built by George Ley in the eighteenth century with his winnings from a card game - the design gives a clue to the name of this former gambling house. Originally it had 52 windows, though some were later blocked to avoid window tax (can you identify the original 52?), each storey decreases in size as the building gets higher, chimneys spout from every corner, there are four floors corresponding to the four suits in a pack , and each floor has 13 doors - an amazing monument in celebration of good fortune at cards.

4 With the Totnes House Detectives

5 A La Ronde is a unique 16-sided house, designed in 1795 by and built in 1796 for two cousins, Jane and Mary Parminter, with stunning views over the Exe estuary, and modelled on San Vitale in Ravenna. On their return from a 'Grand Tour' of Europe, the two ladies incorporated many of the architectural features that had impressed them on their travels and spent the next 13 years decorating each of the rooms and a gallery with every kind of Regency craft - shells and feathers, silhouettes and needlework, sand and seaweed art, mirrors and glass and cut paper - typical of those utilised by ladies of leisure in the eighteenth century.

6 Knightshayes Court, a splendid Victorian mansion surrounded by some of the finest gardens in the country. It was built originally for John Heathcoat Amory MP, grandson of the John Heathcoat who first brought prosperity to Tiverton. Knightshayes was the location for Baskerville Hall in the film of *The Hound of the Baskervilles*.

7 Bowden House, Totnes, which dates back to the ninth century and became well-known as the residence of the De Bloase family, builders of thirteenth-century Totnes Castle.

8 Nineteen

9 Compton Castle, Marldon, Paignton.

10 (a) Leonard Elmhirst and his American heiress wife Dorothy. The name of the estate has become known in many contexts, such as Dartington Glass, and Dartington Pottery established in 1984 to manufacture pottery designed by Janice Tchalenko.

(b) High Cross House.

11 He bought an estate and designed a house at Watcombe, Torbay, but became ill when building the Royal Albert Bridge over the River Tamar, and died soon afterwards.

12 This timber-framed veteran dating to *c.* 1430 and believed to be one of the oldest of its kind in the world, was moved bodily for a hundred yards up Edmund Street to make way for the city's new bypass.

16 INDUSTRY AND EMPLOYMENT

1 Great Torrington

2 At Brannam Pottery, Barnstaple.

3 (a) Honiton

(b) Beer's lace-makers rivalled those of Honiton for quality, a skill brought by refugees from the Netherlands. Queen Victoria's wedding dress was made from Beer lace - taking 100 ladies eight months to make it at a cost of £1,000!

(c) John Heathcoat (1783-1861) first patented the machine, which he invented in 1808. He also invented ribbon- and net-making machinery. Though born in Derby, Heathcoat's first lace factory was at Loughborough but was attacked by a mob of drunken Luddites. Consequently, in 1816 he walked the 200 miles to Tiverton, moved his production there and created employment and prosperity for the town. The factory and business are still thriving and several of Heathcoat's original machines can be seen in Tiverton Museum.

4 Honiton

5 Finch Foundry in Sticklepath, near South Zeal. Once seven waterwheels harnessed the power of the river, with a woollen mill producing serge at the west end, a corn mill at the other, and the Finch brothers in the centre. Here three waterwheels drove machinery producing edge tools for agricultural use and mining - sickles, scythes and shovels.

6 Barnstaple; the pottery takes its name from the Roman name of the town, *Barumensis*.

7 Hydro-electricity is generated in the wooded Glen Lyn Gorge - though the power of water rushing down the valley in 1952 destroyed Lynmouth.

8 At the Tannery, King Street, Colyton. This is the traditional method of tanning and produces a high quality leather for specialised uses.

9 (a) Tavistock, Chagford, Ashburton and Plympton. An early record of tax paid showed that 40% of the county's smelted tin production passed through Chagford.

(b) Tin-miners financed the rebuilding of many churches in the district, and their emblem of three rabbits each carved with two ears but a total of three ears only (honestly!) can be found in them, such as on roof bosses at St Michael's, Chagford, and St Mary the Virgin, Throwleigh

10 Having seen huge Turkish carpets '*ornamented with large figures and without a seam*', in 1755 Thomas Whitty succeeded in producing one measuring 16 feet by 12 feet, helped '*by the pliant fingers of little children.*' The carpet caused a sensation and within thirty years there were Axminster carpets in both Windsor Castle and the White House. The Guildhall, Axminster, contains a piece of Axminster carpet from c.1755.

11 The last copper mine, at Sticklepath, closed in 1925.

12 The pit, which was developed in 1800, is at Lee Moor, at the south-western corner of Dartmoor National Park. The production of 1 ton of kaolin produces 8 tons of waste mica, so huge spoil heaps disfigure a large area surrounding the pit.

17 LITERATURE

1 (a) The fictional Hempsley Cavern is an almost exact description of Kents Cavern, near Torquay, with its cave paintings and flint deposits.
(b) *And Then There Were None* and *Evil Under The Sun*
2 (a) *Westward Ho!*, which gave its name to the adjacent resort (b) *Stalky and Co*
3 (a) Near Canal Bridge on the River Torridge (b) *Salar the Salmon*
4 *Queen Mab*
5 *Brideshead Revisited*
6 *The Hound of the Baskervilles*, the first instalment of which appeared in 1901.
7 R D Blackmore, who spent much time in the tiny village of Charles near South Molton and later stayed at the Royal Oak at Winsford, where he actually wrote part of the novel. The Doone Valley of the novel was inspired by Lank Combe, near Malmsmead.
8 John Galsworthy
9 Michael Morpurgo
10 The long flight of steps to the harbour get a mention in *The Tale of Little Pig Robinson.*
11 At Kitley House, Yealhampton, where she was a regular visitor; the rhyme is believed to be based on the estate's housekeeper, who retired to the cottage, now a restaurant.
12 *The Pickwick Papers*

18 MISCELLANY

1 At Gittisham, near Honiton. She died in Marylebone, London, on 27 December 1814.
2 'Tranquil'
3 Cleave Mill
4 (a) Exonians (b) Isca Dumnoniorum (c) Exanceaster
5 The centenary of the first instalment of Conan Doyle's *The Hound of the Baskervilles*, published in 1901, set on mist-shrouded autumnal Dartmoor. Also in 1901 Abbot Anscav began work on restoring Buckfast Abbey.
6 This spectacular event is held in Plymouth during the first week of August.
7 Dartmouth, where the tradition has grown up that future Kings of England serve as cadets. The present college is very different from the original Britannia which was moored in the River Dart in 1863.
8 The octagonal Pepper Pot, the most distinctive of the town's many historic buildings, is the old market house in the middle of the square at Chagford. Dating from the mid- nineteenth century, it was modelled on the Abbot's Kitchen at Glastonbury.
9 Ashbury, Lewdown, Lifton, Lewtrenchard and Bratton Clovelly.
10 The survey revealed that 70% of parishes still had a pub; it revealed also that an average pub will inject £64,000 a year into the local economy, excluding wages.
11 (a) The machine was invented by Otto Overbeck, a research chemist, and is at his house near Salcombe. Overbeck claimed that the electrical rejuvenator could tone and cure "*all illnesses ... with the exception of malformation and germ diseases.*"
(b) Near Sidmouth - you can watch heavenly bodies at a 'Skywatch Evening'.
12 Okehampton

19 MUSEUMS AND HERITAGE

1 Lynmouth, where it houses a collection of over 100 brasses and rubbing plates.
2 It is the birthplace of Daniel Boone's father.
3 At the Combe Martin Motorcycle Collection
4 In Tiverton Museum.
5 Hartland Quay Museum
6 The Finch Foundry Museum at Sticklepath and Okehampton's Museum of Dartmoor Life, where you can learn about Dartmoor, its people and their ways.
7 Paignton

8 The Museum, holding a vast variety of fish and sharks, is in Rope Walk, Coxside, Plymouth, and features Moorland Streams, River Estuary, Shore and Shallow Seas, with a Deep Reef of life on the Continental Shelf based on the area around the Eddystone Lighthouse, Coral Seas and a Shark Theatre.
9 The collection is at Yelverton.
10 The Butterwalk, Totnes.
11 Seaton Toll Bridge, opened in 1877 over the River Axe, was designed by Philip Brennan and built by local landowner Sir William Trevelyan. The single-storey toll house is also built of concrete, an early example of the use of this material for housing.
12 It was performed at the Royal Bijou Theatre, Paignton.

20 MYTHS AND LEGENDS

1 Sir Francis Drake (1540-1596), Elizabethan explorer and scourge of the Spanish Main, became a living legend through his exploits. An old side drum, measuring under 24 inches high and embellished with his coat of arms, accompanied him on his last voyage to the West Indies. Drake died of dysentry during the voyage, but the drum was brought back to England and housed at Buckland Abbey, his former home halfway between his Tavistock birthplace and home port of Plymouth. There have been reports of the drum beating on its own to warn the nation of threatening events - so if you hear a banging ...!
2 The ghost is the 'Spanish Lady', a young Lieutenant's fiancee who disguised herself as a sailor so she could travel with her love on the ill-fated 1588 Armada expedition. Both were captured and held prisoner with the other 357 Spanish sailors in the barn: she fell ill and died, but he recovered and returned to Spain. Her ghost can be heard crying and sobbing for her love.
3 The ghost of fierce Hubba the Dane, who was buried here after promising to 'waste with fire and sword' the good folk of Appledore - he lost, but do tip-toe past the Wibblestone lest you wake his ghost!
4 Virgins visiting the Inn on New Year's Eve may see the face of their future husband in the smoke of the pub's ashwood fire.
5 It is the astronomical clock in Exeter Cathedral.
6 The gilded roof boss depicting a sow feeding her farrow illustrates the legend of how the church was founded by St Brannoc, who came from Wales as an evangelist in AD 550 having floated over the sea on a stone coffin. An angel told him to build the church where a sow was suckling her litter - which he did, and a church stands here today.
7 Because the spire has a marked twist. A bride who came to the church was so beautiful that the spire bowed to her - and for this over-familiar gesture has been in a permanent stoop ever since. Others try to explain that unseasoned timbers have twisted unevenly over the years - but we know better, don't we?
8 It was built there to be out of the Devil's reach, for at night he had been demolishing the building work on the original site on lower ground.
9 Bideford, in Bridgeland Street.
10 The legend says that a trio of spinsters (spinning women) erected the Neolithic tomb one morning before breakfast to amuse themselves when they were taking their spun wool to the collecting agent. The name dates from medieval times when the wool trade was a very significant cottage industry.
11 The hole in the boulder in the river bed was worn by friction of the water. Those who climb onto the rock and drop through unscathed to the slab below will be immune to all rheumatic complaints - a procedure not advisable when the river is in full spate!
12 Kitty Jay was the daughter of a tenant farmer who fell in love with the landowner's son. Seduced by tales of love and marriage, she spent a night with the boy only to be told the following morning that he would never marry such a low-born girl. Kitty returned home and hanged herself in her father's barn, was not allowed a Christian burial and was buried at a cross-roads so her spirit, confused by the number of roads, would not wander. Years later, a man excavated the grave and found it did indeed contain the skeleton of a young woman; he arranged for the simple headstone that still stands here. This might have been the end of the story, but flowers are regularly placed on the grave by a ghostly hand, and those who stay here at night to try to watch are driven away by unseen terrors before the flowers arrive.

21 POLITICAL AFFAIRS

1 In the Combat Collection at Cobbaton

2 Musbury, in 1650.

3 (a) Slapton Sands, which was considered ideal for such an operation.

(b) The obelisk was erected as thanks to the 3,000 local people who within 6 weeks gave up their homes to provide a battle practice area in 1944 for the Normandy landings, as live ammunition was use

(c) A Sherman tank salvaged from the sea stands in memory of more than a thousand American troops who were killed in a D-Day rehearsal disaster. Some died on the beach when they were landed before the naval bombardment ended, and 709 were drowned when an American landing craft convoy ran into a group of German E-boats in Start Bay, and was torpedoed.

4 In December 1819 the Duke and Duchess of Kent, with the infant Princess Victoria, arrived at Woolcombe Cottage, now the Royal Glen Hotel. Their stay was tragically short, for the Duke died on 23 January from complications after a heavy cold. Then his father, George III, died only six days later. Before then there had been another dramatic event. Playing in her room, Princess Victoria was narrowly missed by a gunshot fired by a young man hunting birds - the replacement pane of coloured glass can still be seen.

5 Hatherleigh was the birthplace of Colonel William Morris who led the Charge of the Light Brigade.

6 They can be seen at Sheepstor. The first, James Brooke, went to Sarawak as an official to thank the Rajah for his kindness to a group of ship-wrecked British sailors. Finding the country over-run by pirates, he restored peace and was made Rajah by the grateful inhabitants. He was succeeded to the title by two other members of the Brooke family.

7 In 1859, when the expansionist tendencies of Louis Napoleon's Second Empire were considered a threat to British security, Prime Minister Lord Palmerston ordered the building of several forts and batteries around Plymouth, a dockyard second only to Portsmouth. Work began in 1862. The North-Eastern Defences alone consisted of seven forts, three batteries and a keep. The most important was Crownhill Fort which has tunnels, gun emplacements and working cannon. Such a huge sum was spent in preparing for an attack that never came that the forts were known as 'Palmerston's follies'.

8 Sir Humphrey Gilbert, founder of the colony of Newfoundland, Adrian Gilbert who discovered the north-west passage, and (by her second husband) Sir Walter Raleigh.

9 Barnstaple is the oldest borough, and Totnes, founded by the Vikings in the early 900s, is the second oldest; its first mayor was elected in 1359.

10 This bit of Devon was given to Ontario State in 1966 by the then owner of Wolford House, Sir Geoffrey Harmsworth. The house was once the home of General John Graves Simcoe (1752-1806) who fought in the War of American Independence. He bought Wolford Estate in 1784 and in 1791was appointed the first Lieutenant General of the newly formed Province of Upper Canada, and founded the town of York, which later became Ontario. In 1806 he was appointed Commander-in-Chief of India, but died before he could take up the post and was buried in the little church he had built only in 1800.

11 (a) Brixham, where the statue of William of Orange at Harbourside is the only one of him in England with a Dutch inscription.

(b) The stone has been preserved and only two other people have stood on it - William IV (as the Duke of Clarence) and our present Queen in July 1988.

12 The people in Tavistock claim that the one in Plymouth is a copy of their's.

22 PUBS

1 The Royal Clarence, Exeter, which in 1769 was the first inn to describe itself a 'hotel', French-style.

2 Through burning a signal fire whenever Revenue Officers were about - smuggling in the South Hams brought in more brandy and rum than legally through the Port of London!

3 Those fourteenth-century locals who were given the right to cut gorse for fuel to boil pots.

4 (a) The Warren House Inn, alongside the B3212 two miles north-west of Postbridge. The inn was built for the miners who daily during the nineteenth-century trudged down the path to work in the Dagg Valley below, and takes its name from one of the extensive warrens, or game preserves, on medieval Dartmoor, in this instance Headland Warren.

(b) A century ago Warren House Inn was the home of Jonas Coaker, who described himself as 'the poet of the moor.' He moved the pub from its original site on the opposite side of the road - a move strangely lacking in business sense. There the pub stood on common land and was free of rent. When he crossed the road Jonas moved onto land owned by the Duchy of Cornwall and ended up paying rent!

5 (a) The Pilchard Inn, a notorious meeting place for thieves and smugglers in years gone by. Most notable of these was Tom Crocker, who was shot dead by a revenue officer after a life of wrecking, plundering and smuggling.
(b) 1336 (c) 282 metres

6 The Beer Engine is a combined pub and brewery, serving its own home-brewed beers.

7 It is at Woodbury. Much of the church dates from Saxon times times, but at the end of the fourteenth century the tower was added. The masons who built it also built the White Hart for their own accommodation - making it the oldest White Hart in the country.

8 Gara Rock Hotel on the East Portlemouth peninsula and situated 320 feet high on a cliff overlooking miles of unspoilt coastline.

9 Built in 1380, it is Dartmouth's oldest surviving building.

10 The Puffing Billy

11 It is at Doddiscombsleigh.

12 The Bishop Blaize Inn.

23 RECORD BREAKERS

1 Westward Ho!

2 Exmouth was the first 'watering-place' in Devon, in the late eighteenth century, but was eclipsed by Torquay when the railway reached it first.

3 In Kingsbridge - see if you can squeeze through it!

4 Brixham Berry Head Lighthouse

5 It is Parliament Street, Exeter.

6 Combe Martin

7 Barricane Beach, Woolacombe

8 Castle Drogo, built between 1910 and 1930.

9 You will find 2,010 garden gnomes, of every description from those portraying children to very old men, at the home of Mrs Ann Atkin, in West Putford, North Devon.

10 Salcombe - its southerly location is evident in its climate.

11 On Great Torrington Commons where there was a life-size re-enactment of the Great Fire of London. Twenty enthusiasts spent hundreds of hours building a full-scale replica of seventeenth-century City of London, complete with Pudding Lane Bakery, brothels, a prison and old St Paul's - and started the fire, authentically, at 8.30pm

12 Canonteign Falls, where the Lady Exmouth falls are 220 feet high.

24 SAINTS AND SINNERS

1 At 1300 feet above sea level, Princetown was considered to be a perfect place to build a prison. Thomas Tyrwitt was born in Essex in 1762, and when studying at Oxford became a friend of the Prince of Wales (later George IV) who in 1797 made him Secretary and Keeper of the Privy Seal. Tyrwitt arrived on Dartmoor in 1785 and began to create a large estate and establish 'Prince's Town'. In 1786 he was appointed Auditor to the Duchy and later as a Member of Parliament rose to become Lord Warden of the Stannaries. In 1805, aware of the shocking conditions in which Napoleonic war prisoners were confined aboard hulks at Plymouth, Tyrwitt conceived the idea of a prison on the moor. With the Prince's approval work proceeded and soon French and American prisoners (from the war of 1812) were accommodated. After they departed in 1815 the prison stood empty but in 1850 was re-opened as a civil prison. Tyrwitt died in 1833. It is owned by the Duchy of Cornwall, which earns a healthy sum from its lease on it.

2 Totnes

3 This was the name given to Bob Eliot, an eighteenth-century smuggler from Brixham who evaded the Customs by 'dying' and spiriting away his contraband in his coffin.

4 (a) In the garden of the vicarage at Tavistock (next to the Bedford Hotel)
(b) The young nun was loved by a monk - did he murder her out of guilt or rejection?
5 St Boniface (c.680-754) was born Wynfrith in Crediton.
6 (a) This small fortress pre-dated the existing castle in 1388, and John Hawley, mayor of Dartmouth, was one of the town's most 'colourful' merchants.
(b) He is considered to be the inspiration for 'The Shipman' in 'A Shipman's Tale' in Chaucer's *The Canterbury Tales*.
7 In the novel it was the Inn where Salvation Yeo killed the King of the Gubbins tribe - no name was more feared on Dartmoor - who actually lived in Lydford Gorge during the reign of Charles I. They were a band of sheep and cattle thieves as notorious for their red beards as for their ruthless pillaging of local farms and cottages and evaded capture by hiding out and living like animals in the many dark caves and glens.
8 (a) Although it looks like an ordinary Norman castle keep, it was built in 1195 as a courtroom and prison from which 'Lydford Law' was administered, initially to those caught poaching in the King's Forest of Dartmoor.
(b) Later it was used by the tin miners to house offenders against the ruthless and arbitrary Stannary Laws - some found guilty of adulterating tin had molten metal spooned down their throats - but also to imprison any-one with whom they disagreed, including one local MP, Richard Strode, who complained about mining debris in moorland rivers silting Plymouth's harbour and tried to promote a Bill which would curb their powers. 'Lydford Law' had an ill reputation:

First hang and draw
Then hear the cause, is Lydford Law.

9 A pillory.
10 In 1885 John Lee of Babbacombe was convicted of murdering his employer, but despite three attempts at hanging him at Exeter Gaol was released after serving a long sentence and lived to a ripe old age.
11 It was named after Jennifred de Wichehalse who was jilted in the 1680s by Lord Auberley, and hurled herself from the cliff.
12 Richard Cabell, a seventeenth-century squire of Buckfastleigh, who is said to have bred a pack of huge, fierce dogs and hunted them on Dartmoor, little caring whether the quarry was deer, fox or one of his tenants. When he died in 1677 the locals erected a tomb with a heavy slab and an iron grille to prevent his spirit from haunting the neighbourhood. In reality Cabell does not seem to have been particularly wicked, and his story only came into vogue after publication of the novel on 1901, perhaps to cash in on its popularity.

24 SPORT

1 It is held in March in the Axe Valley.
2 (a) A Championship Course (b) Royal North Devon Golf Club course, Westward Ho!
3 (a) Supposedly following in the footsteps of treasure seekers, it is a network of ten walks, some coastal, from Exeter to Kingswear linked together by bus and rail services.
(b) A challenging 100-mile cycling route from Axmouth to the Blackdown Hills.
4 Arlington Court, near Barnstaple
5 (a) 38 miles (b) a foxglove
6 Warren Golf Club, Dawlish Warren
7 (a) The Devon and Exeter Racecourse and the Newton Abbot Racecourse.
(b) Agatha Christie's favourite horse-racing course was the Haldon. During the 1950s the 'Mousetrap Handicap' was started, named after her famous stage play. Each year she presented the trophy to the winner, now undertaken by her daughter or grandson.
8 Sue Barker
9 It is held at Totnes.
10 (a) the Grecians (b) the Chiefs
11 The Championships are held in Paignton.
12 The Dartmoor Ten Tors Walk.

25 TOWNS AND CITIES

1 Torquay, in 1890
2 Hatherleigh
3 Its original name came about because salt was panned from the sea here.
4 Near Devonport, in 1868
5 (a) Blasting for the route began in 1887 and the railway opened in 1890 and was at that time the steepest in the world.
(b) Both cars carry 2½ tons of water to power the movement 475 feet upwards.
6 Charles Babbage (1791-1871) was born at Teignmouth, and went to school at at Totnes. He invented firstly a 'difference engine' and then an 'analytical engine', which were prototype computers.
7 Charles Dickens
8 The Barbican (or Watergate), How Gate in the south wall, Frankfurt Gate in the west wall, and Old Town Gate in the north wall.
9 It is only large enough for one stall and that was specifically for meat. It is a completely open timber-framed structure, 13 feet by 9 feet, with a steeply-pitched slate roof and carved barge-boards, built in the seventeenth century. Now it is used as a wooden seat.
10 (a) The passages are under Exeter High Street.
(b) They were constructed in the fourteenth century to bring fresh water into the heart of the city.
11 The first batch of palm trees was imported to the area in the 1820s, since when they have multiplied into many thousands, some of considerable size, creating a unique atmosphere.
12 Ashburton, with a population of 3,500.

26 TRANSPORT AND COMMUNICATION

1 The Atlantic Highway
2 (a) The picturesque rail link between Barnstaple and Exeter passing through pretty villages and the fertile Taw Valley
(b) They have to: it was one of the conditions demanded by the then Earl of Portsmouth when he sold the land for the construction of this part of the original railway line; it is also where trains have to wait to pass each other before continuing along the stretches of single track.
3 The *Kathleen and May*; a modification had to be made to the restored three masts so that the upper portion of each can be lowered using a block and tackle system. The schooner was refitted at a cost of £750,000, and then visited Youghal, near Cork, her home port for thirty years. The ship was one of the last UK trading schooners, working until 1962.
4 The Seaton Electric Tramway runs from Seaton
(a) along the banks of the river Axe to the villages of Colyford and Colyton;
(b) the gauge of the tramline is two feet and nine inches; (c) thirty years.
5 Exeter, Plymouth
6 (a) The 'atmospheric railway' was vacuum-powered by atmospheric pressure - no smoke, no smell, very little noise and economical to run. Brunel did not invent the system but in 1847 as Director of the South Western Railways Board he commissioned the railway to run between Exeter and Newton Abbot. The directors of the Great Western Railway granted a quarter of a million pounds to pay for it. In the 1840s that was enough to cover the laying of the track and the erection of 10 large pumping stations along the route. A pipe ran between the rails, connected to the pumping stations, with a slot along the top covered by leather flaps. A piston under the train fitted into the slot, and this was literally sucked along the pipe. After it had passed, the leather flaps would close the gap again and make it airtight. The trials were a success, trains reaching speeds of 70 mph hauling loads of 28 tons. Alas, the leather flaps caused problems and could not make the pipe air-tight after the train had gone through. The leather was affected by the climate and the salt sea air, and greasing them with whale and seal oil only attracted the local rat population, which gnawed away the flaps while some were sucked into the vacuum and landed up in the engine room. In 1848 Brunel, uncharacteristically, admitted defeat. Steam engines returned.
(b) It ran between Exeter and Newton Abbot, though the original plan was that it should run as far as Totnes. One of the pumping stations on England's only 'atmospheric railway' remains at Starcross, and is now a museum.
7 Sixteen

8 The South Devon Railway, which runs from Buckfastleigh to Totnes.
9 At Devon Railway Centre, Bickleigh Bridge, near Tiverton.
10 The Grade II listed former toll house is in Yealmbridge, 8 miles from Plymouth.
11 Instow
12 MS *Oldenburg*

27 VILLAGES

1 (a) Clovelly, where the main street was built on the dry bed of a stream. The village is regarded as amongst the world's most unique because its picturesque cobbled streets tumble steeply down the cliffside to a fourteenth-century harbour.
(b) In 1738, after the last generation of the Cary family, who had owned the village since c. 1370, died childless, Clovelly was sold to the Hamlyn family. It was Christine Hamlyn, who died in 1936 aged 80, who devised the policies to keep Clovelly unspoiled by tourism. Many of the cottages bear her initials and a date showing when they were refurbished at her expense. She forbade anyone to put up hoardings, build new bungalows or hotels, or set up ice-cream or souvenir stalls.
2 Combe Martin
3 (a) 'Ditsum' (b) 'Woolsery'
4 'The Little Switzerland of England'.
5 In the quiet, unspoilt village of Sidbury.
6 The two villages are related in two ways: they are linked by the river Tavy and both names derive from their respective parish church, so we have 'St Mary's on the river Tavy' while its neighbour centres similarly on its own parish church of St Peter.
7 Belstone - where the unusual post office was once a chapel and the village stocks have been retained - but not in use!
8 He was born at Holne, where his father was the rector for a time.
9 The small village of Street Undercliffe, which stood here, was destroyed in a great gale of 1708.
10 A yew tree.
11 Cockington, near Torquay.
12 Twenty-six parishes, each of which has chosen a letter of the alphabet reflecting something special about their community - eg Sheepwash has chosen 'S' not from its name but for the medieval strip fields on the outskirts of the village. An individually crafted pottery plaque has been erected in a discreet place in each village for visitors to discover, and a 'passport control' set up where they can get their 'passport' stamped with a replica of the plaque.